Top Chart Hits

I CAN
PLAY
THAT!™

Wise Publications
London/New York/Paris/Sydney/
Copenhagen/Madrid/Tokyo

2·216916·21

Exclusive Distributors:
Music Sales Limited
8/9 Frith Street, London W1V 5TZ, England.
Music Sales Pty Limited
120 Rothschild Avenue, Rosebery, NSW 2018, Australia.

Order No. AM962940
ISBN 0-7119-8054-3
This book © Copyright 2000 by Wise Publications

Compiled by Nick Crispin
Music arranged by Stephen Duro
Music processed by Allegro Reproductions
Cover photograph (Robbie Williams) courtesy of Rex Features

Printed in the United Kingdom by
Halstan & Co Limited, Amersham, Buckinghamshire.

Your Guarantee of Quality
As publishers, we strive to produce every book to the highest commercial standards.
The music has been freshly engraved and the book has been carefully designed to minimise
awkward page turns and to make playing from it a real pleasure.
Particular care has been given to specifying acid-free, neutral-sized paper made from pulps
which have not been elemental chlorine bleached. This pulp is from farmed sustainable forests
and was produced with special regard for the environment.
Throughout, the printing and binding have been planned to ensure a sturdy, attractive publication
which should give years of enjoyment.
If your copy fails to meet our high standards, please inform us and we will gladly replace it.

Music Sales' complete catalogue describes thousands of titles and is available in full colour sections
by subject, direct from Music Sales Limited. Please state your areas of interest
and send a cheque/postal order for £1.50 for postage to:
Music Sales Limited, Newmarket Road, Bury St. Edmunds, Suffolk IP33 3YB.

www.musicsales.com

Baby One More Time

Words & Music by Max Martin

Moderately

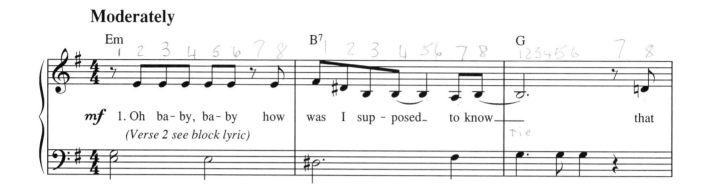

1. Oh ba-by, ba-by how was I sup-posed to know_____ that
(Verse 2 see block lyric)

some-thin' was-n't right here? Oh ba-by, ba-by I should-n't have let____ you go.____

____ And now you're out of sight yeah. Show me how you want it

to be. Tell me ba-by 'cos I need to know now oh, be-cause____

My lone - li - ness is kill - in' me and__ I,__ __ I must con - fess I

still be - lieve,__ still be - lieve.__ When I'm not with you I lose my mind. Give me a sign,__

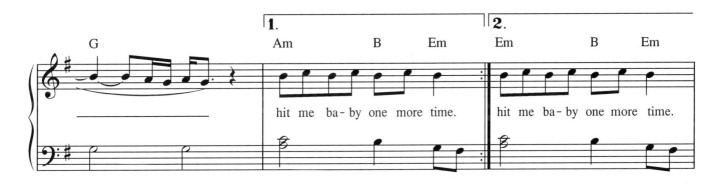

1.
__ __ hit me ba - by one more time.

2.
hit me ba - by one more time.

Oh ba - by, ba - by. Oh, oh.__ Oh ba - by, ba - by. Ah__ yeah, yeah.

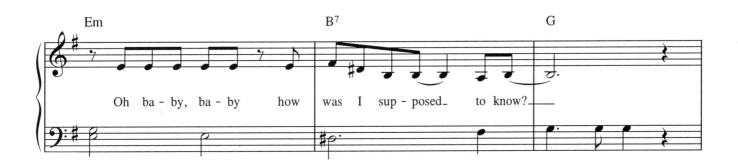

Oh ba - by, ba - by how was I sup - posed__ to know?__

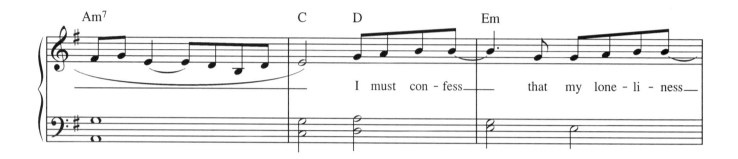

still be - lieve,_____ still be - lieve._____ When I'm not with you I lose

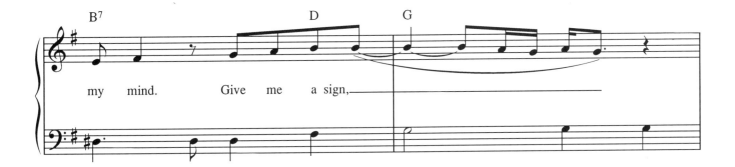

my mind. Give me a sign,_____

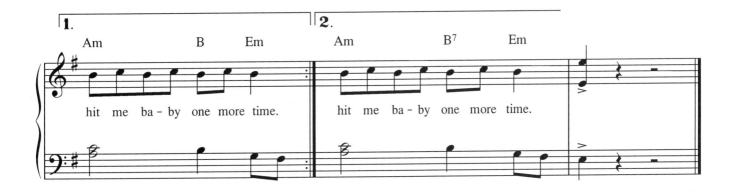

1. hit me ba - by one more time.

2. hit me ba - by one more time.

Verse 2:

Oh baby, baby
The reason I breathe is you
Boy you got me blinded.
Oh pretty baby
There's nothing that I wouldn't do
It's not the way I planned it.

Show me how you want it to be *etc.*

Lift Me Up

**Words & Music by Geri Halliwell, Andy Watkins,
Paul Wilson & Tracy Ackerman**

Moderately

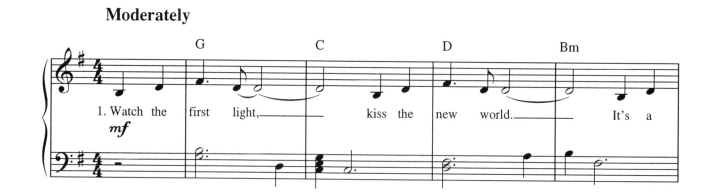

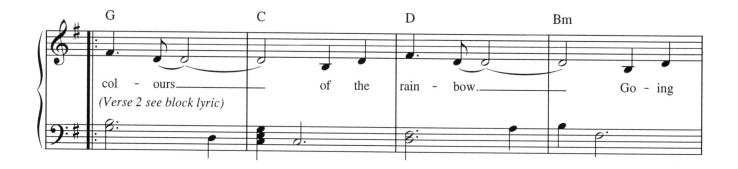

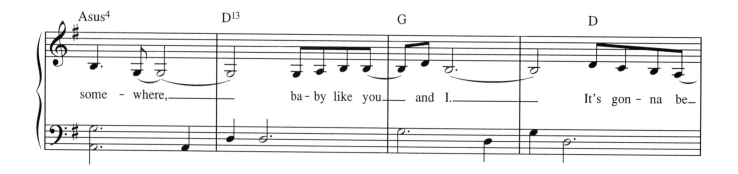

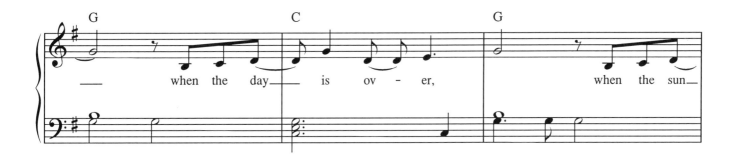

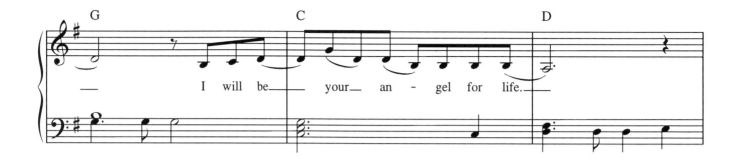

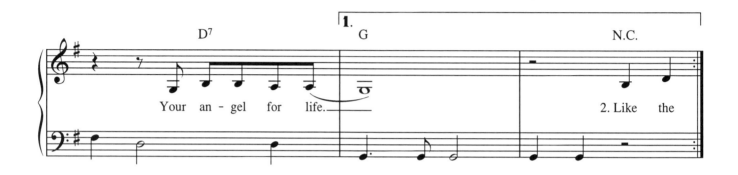

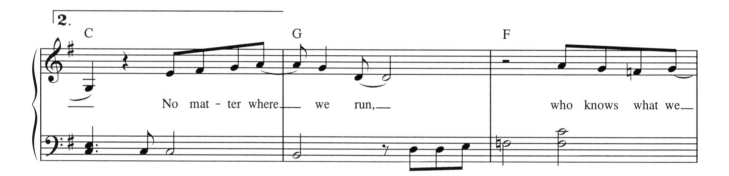

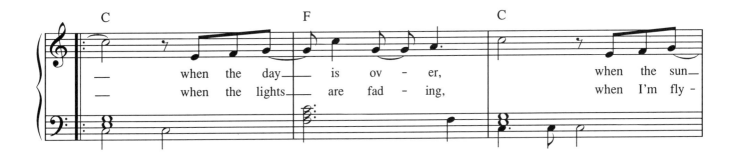

Verse 2:

Like the seasons, ever changing
Everlasting, baby like you and I
It's gonna be alright
But when my sky clouds over

Lift me up *etc.*

If I Could Turn Back The Hands Of Time

Words & Music by R. Kelly

Moderately

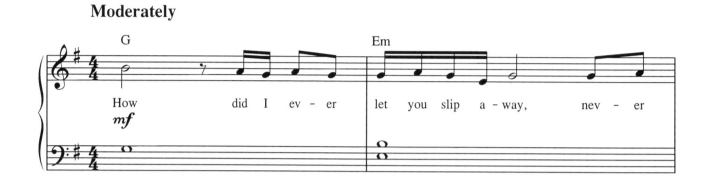

How did I ev - er let you slip a - way, nev - er

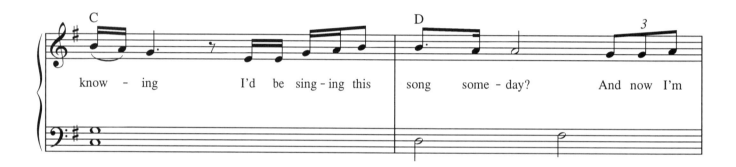

know - ing I'd be sing - ing this song some - day? And now I'm

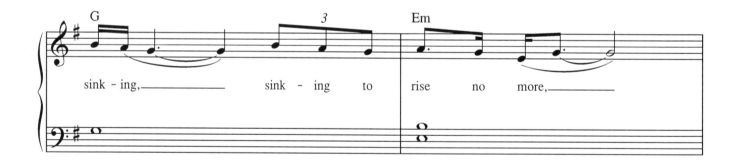

sink - ing,_____ sink - ing to rise no more,_____

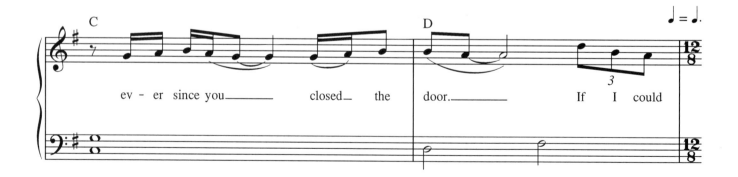

ev - er since you_____ closed__ the door._____ If I could

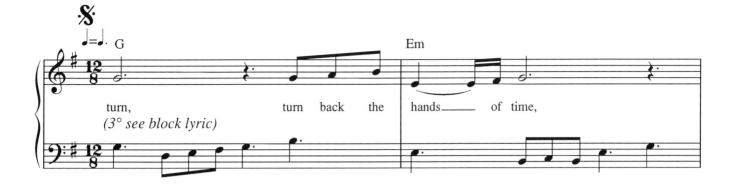

turn,   turn back the   hands   of time,

(3° see block lyric)

then, my dar - ling, you'd   still be   mine,   If I

could turn,   turn   back the hands of time,   then

To Coda I

To Coda II

dar - ling, you'd   you'd   still be   mine.

Fun - ny,   fun - ny   how time goes by

13

and bless-ings___ are missed in the wink of an eye.___ Woah,___ why,

oh, why,_ oh, why___ should one have to go on suf-fer-ing___ when ev-'ry

day___ I plead,___ "Please come back to me?"

D.S. al Coda I

CODA I

If___ I could

mine.___ And

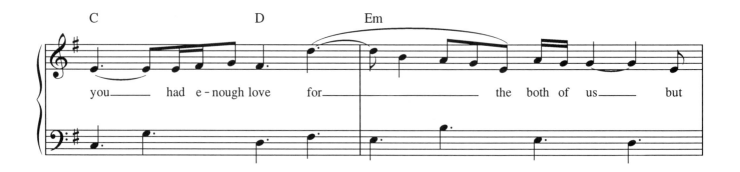

you___ had e-nough love for___ the both of us___ but

I,_____ I,_____ I did you wrong._____ I ad-mit I did,_ but

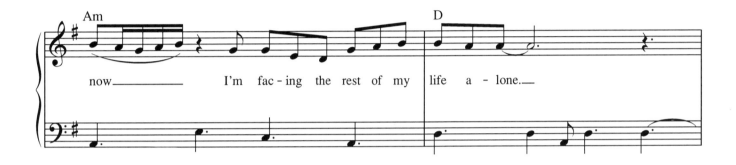

now_____ I'm fac-ing the rest of my life a - lone._

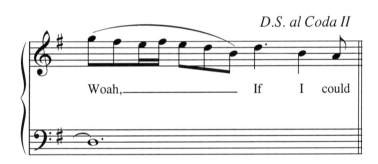

D.S. al Coda II

Woah,_____ If I could

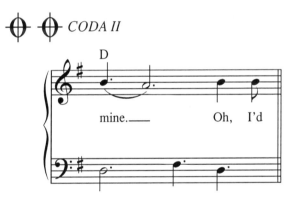

CODA II

mine._ Oh, I'd

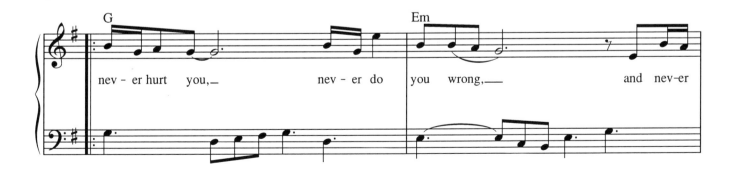

nev - er hurt you,_ nev - er do you wrong,_ and nev-er

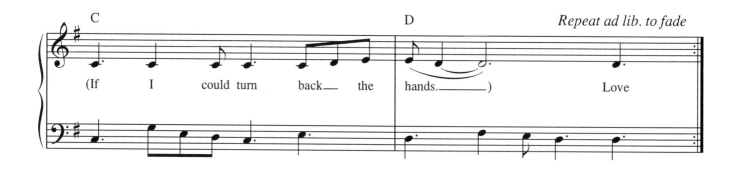

3°:

Woah, if I could just turn back that little clock on the wall
Then I'd come to realise how much I love you.

I Have A Dream

Words & Music by Benny Andersson & Björn Ulvaeus

Moderately

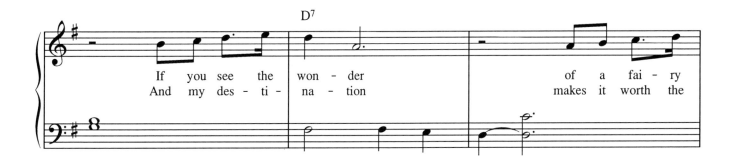

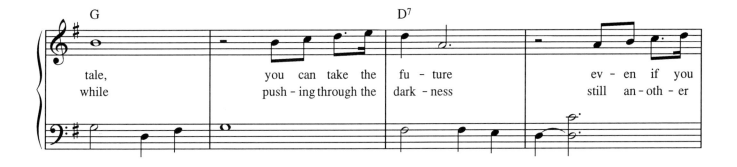

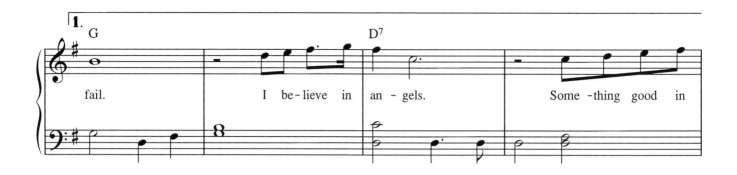

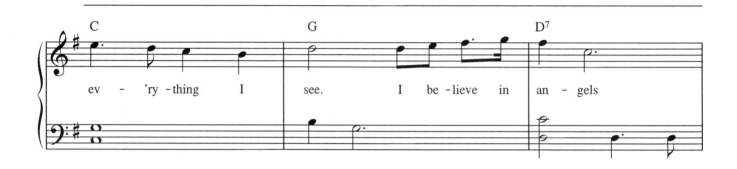

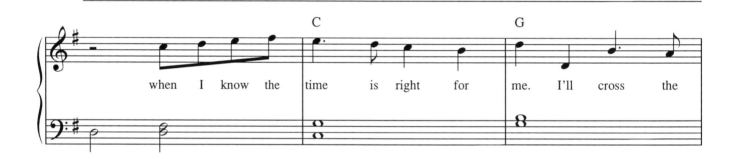

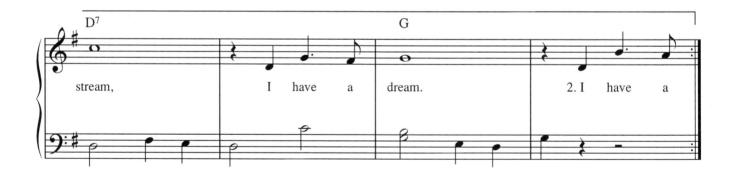

Some-thing good in ev – 'ry -thing I see. I be - lieve in

an – gels when I know the time is right for

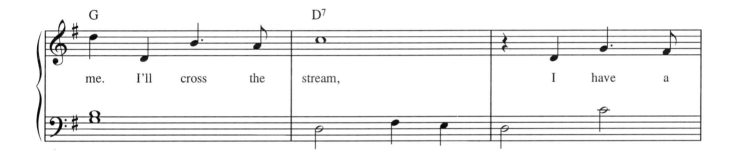

me. I'll cross the stream, I have a

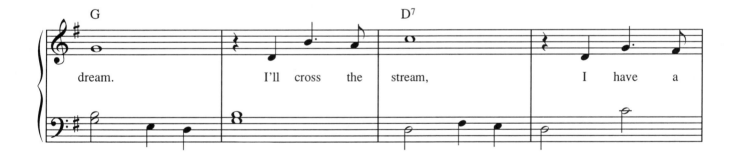

dream. I'll cross the stream, I have a

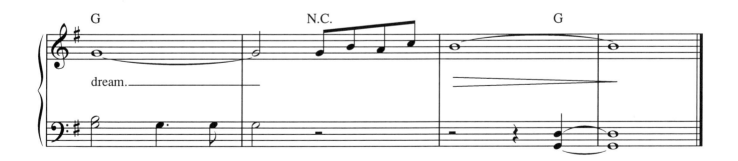

dream.

I Wouldn't Believe Your Radio

Words by Kelly Jones
Music by Kelly Jones, Richard Jones & Stuart Cable

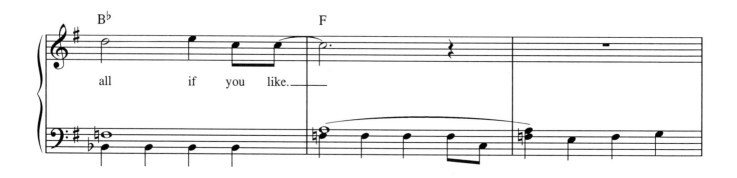

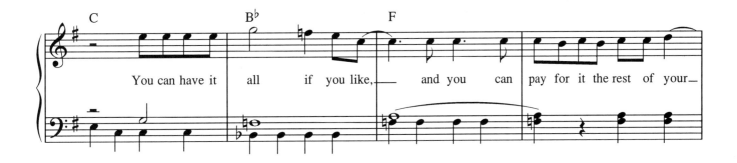

You can have it all if you like,____ and you can pay for it the rest of your___

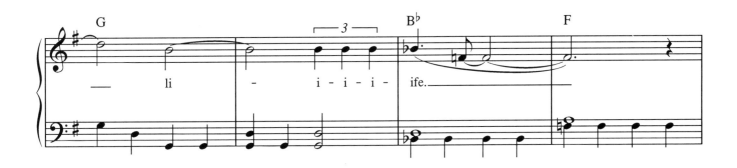

____ li - i - i - i - ife.____

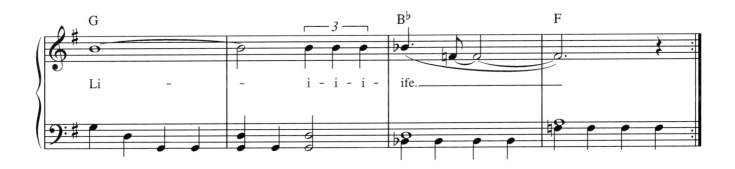

Li - - i - i - i - ife.____

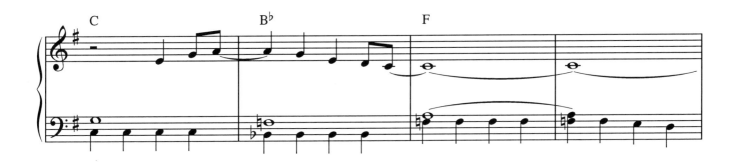

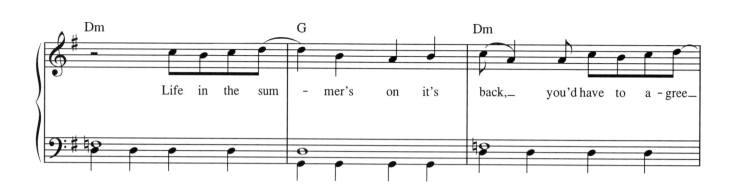

Life in the sum - mer's on it's back,— you'd have to a-gree—

— that that's the crack,— so take what you want,— I'm not com - ing

back.———— So you can have it

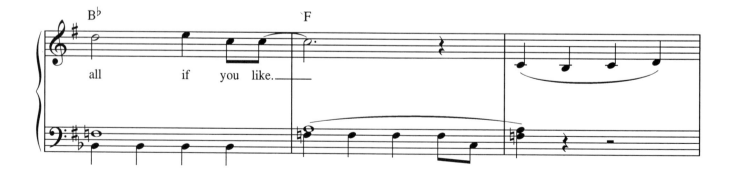

all if you like.————

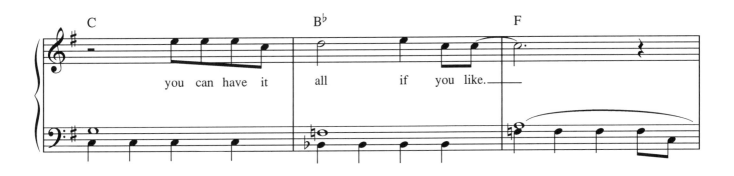

you can have it all if you like.

Oh you can have it all if you like.

You can have it

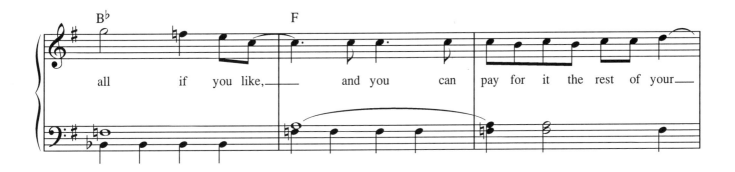

all if you like, and you can pay for it the rest of your

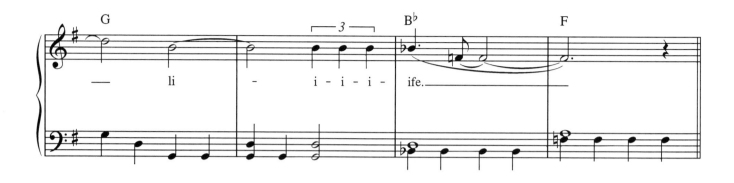

li - - i - i - i - ife.

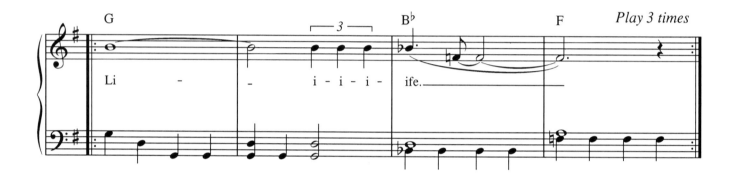

Li - - - i - i - i - ife.

Play 3 times

Verse 2:

I wouldn't believe your wireless radio
If I had myself a flying giraffe
You'd have one in a box with a window.

But you can have it all *etc.*

Radio

Words & Music by Andrea Corr, Caroline Corr, Sharon Corr & Jim Corr

Moderately

1. It's late at night and I'm feel-ing down, there are

(Verse 2 see block lyric)

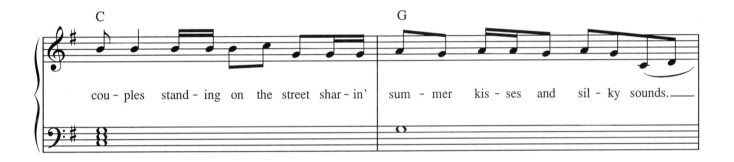

cou-ples stand-ing on the street shar-in' sum-mer kis-ses and sil-ky sounds.

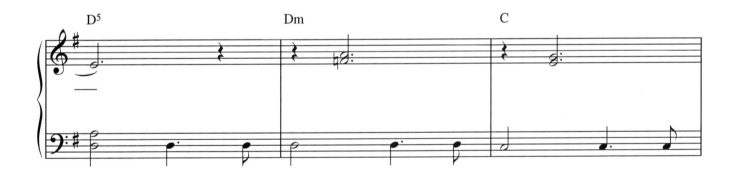

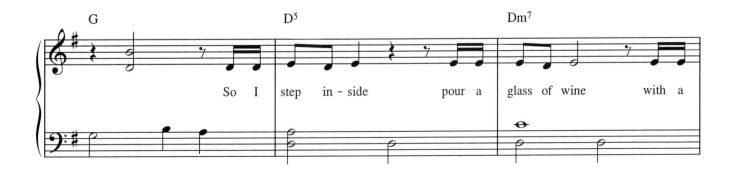

So I step in-side pour a glass of wine with a

full glass and an emp-ty heart I search for some-thing to oc-cu-py my

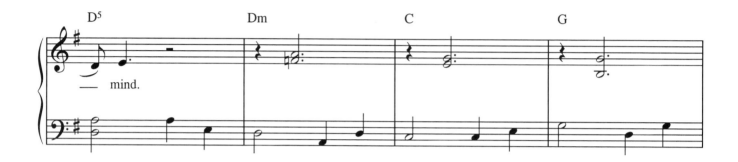

mind.

But you are in my head,

swim-ming for-ev-er in my head. tang-led in my dreams,

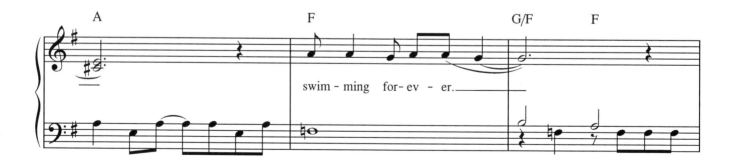

swim-ming for-ev-er.

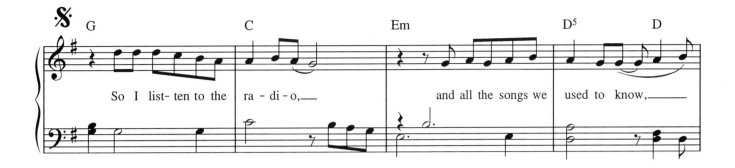

So I list-ten to the ra - di - o,___ and all the songs we used to know,___

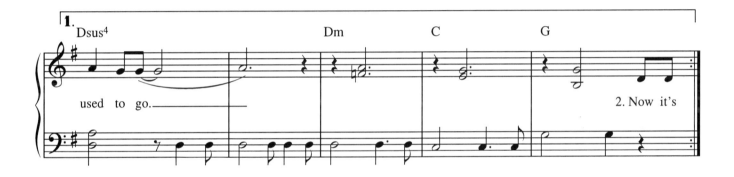

So I list-ten to the ra - di - o,___ re - mem - ber where we

1. used to go.___ 2. Now it's

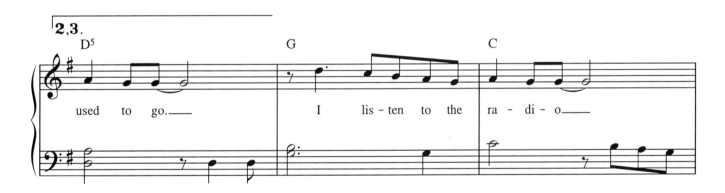

2,3. used to go.___ I lis - ten to the ra - di - o___

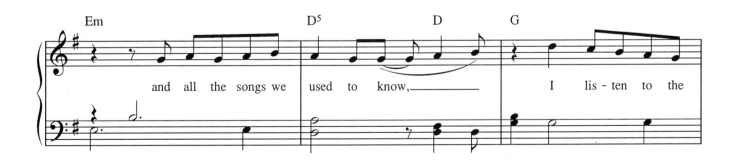

and all the songs we used to know,___ I lis - ten to the

27

ra - di - o___

To Coda ⊕   Em

re - mem - ber how we used to go.___

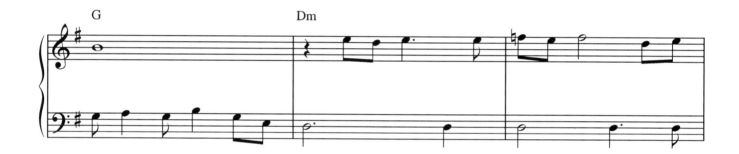

You are in___ my head,___   swim- ming for - ev - er in my___

head.

tang-led in my dreams,

D.S. al Coda

swim-ming for-ev-er,

swim-ming for-ev-er.

CODA

Verse 2:

Now it's morning light and it's cold outside
Caught up in a distant dream
I turn and think that you are by my side
So I leave my bed and I try to dress
Wondering why my mind plays tricks
And fools me in to thinking you are there
But you're just in my head
Swimming forever in my head
Not lying in my bed
Just swimming forever.

So listen to the radio *etc.*

She's The One

Words & Music by Karl Wallinger

1. I was her, she was me, we were one,

we were free. And if there's some-bo-dy call-ing me on,

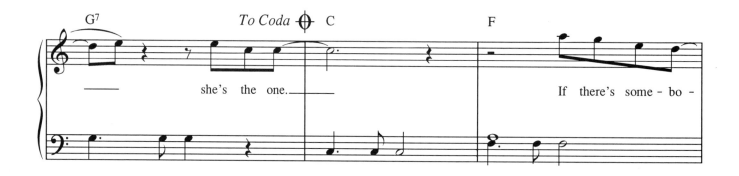

she's the one. If there's some-bo-

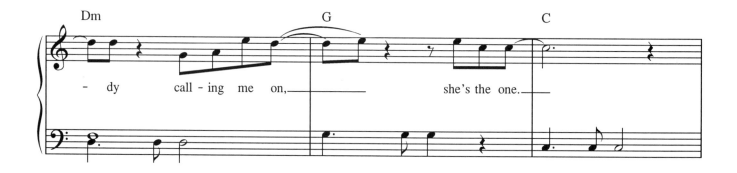

-dy call-ing me on, she's the one.

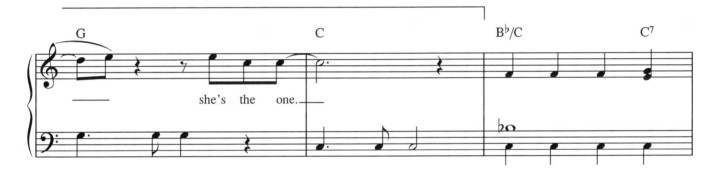

know the way you wan-na play,____ yeah. You'll be so high you'll be

fly ___ ing. 3. Though the sea____ - ing. 4. I was her____

___ If there's some-bo -

- dy call-ing me on,____ she's the one.____

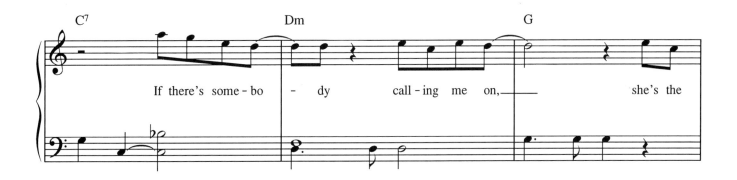

If there's some-bo - dy call-ing me on,___ she's the

one, yes, she's the one.___ If there's some-bo - dy call-ing me on,___

___ she's the one,___ she's the one.__ If there's some-bo -

- dy call-ing me on,___ she's the one,___ she's the

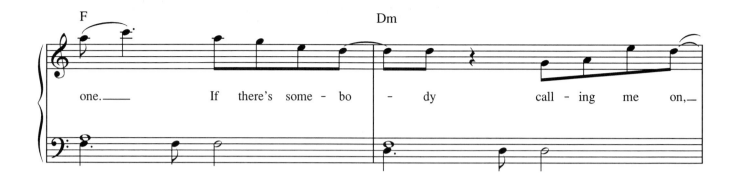

one. _____ If there's some - bo - dy call - ing me on, _

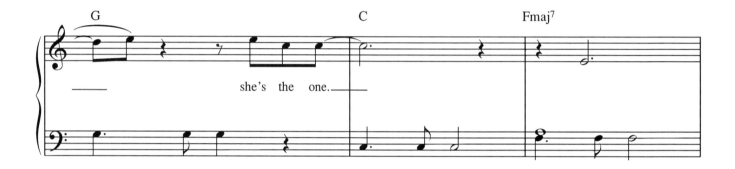

_____ she's the one. _____

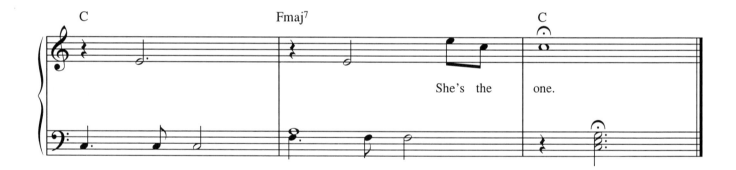

She's the one.

Verse 3:

Though the sea will be strong
I know we'll carry on
'Cos if there's somebody calling me on, she's the one
If there's somebody calling me on, she's the one.

Verse 4:

I was her, she was me
We were one, we were free
And if there's somebody calling me on *etc.*

When You Say Nothing At All

Words & Music by Paul Overstreet & Don Schlitz

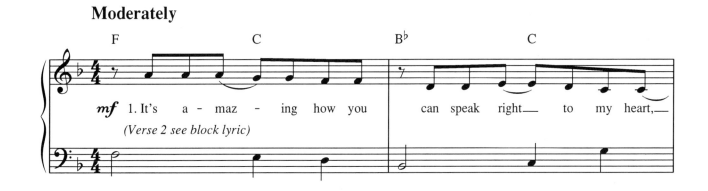

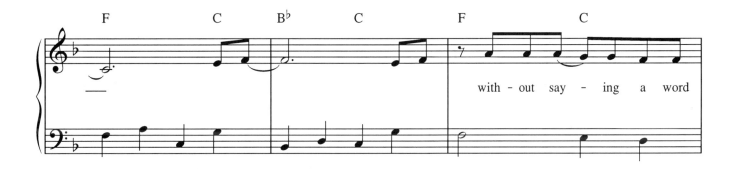

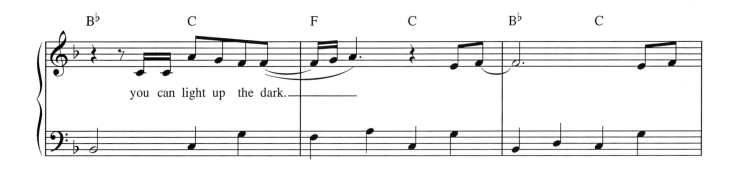

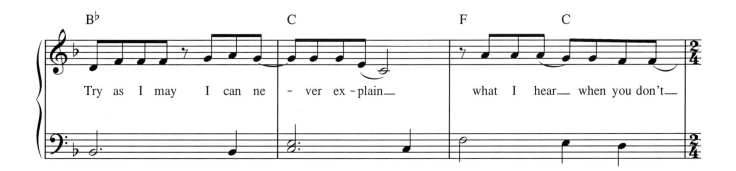

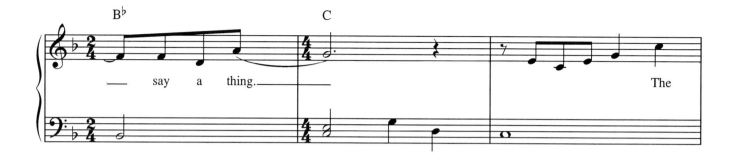

— say a thing.

The

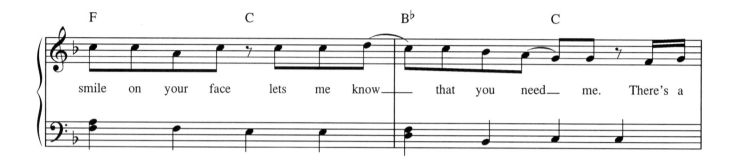

smile on your face lets me know— that you need— me. There's a

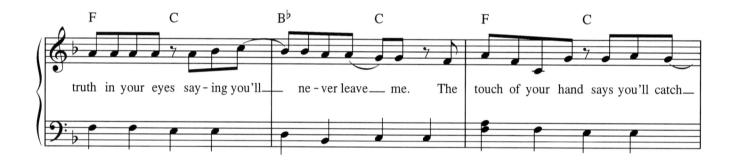

truth in your eyes say - ing you'll— ne - ver leave— me. The touch of your hand says you'll catch—

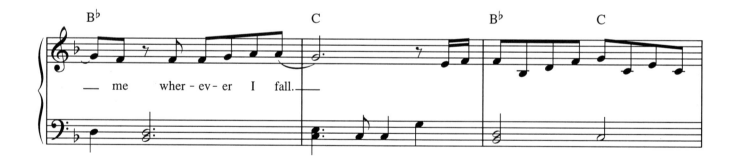

— me wher - ev - er I fall.—

You— say it best when you say no - thing at all.—

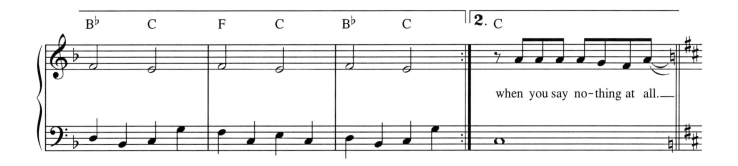

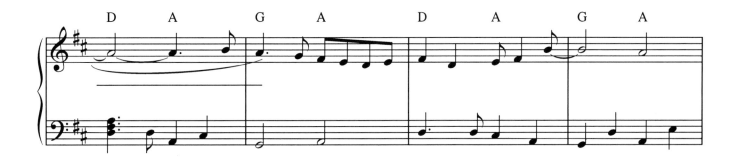

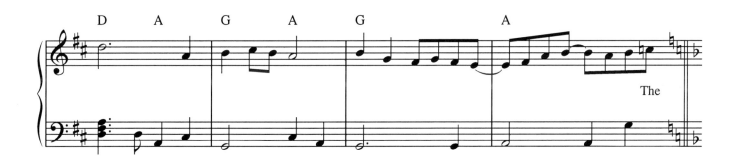

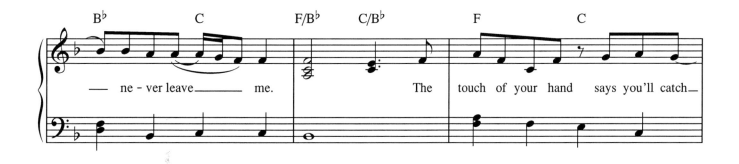

— me wher - ev - er I fall.

You say it best when you say no - thing at all.

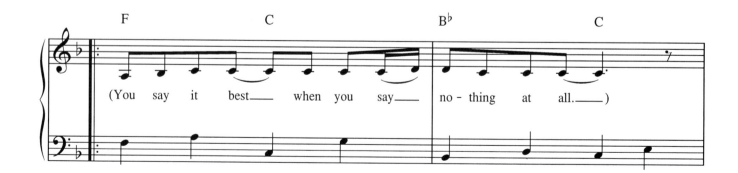

(You say it best when you say no - thing at all.)

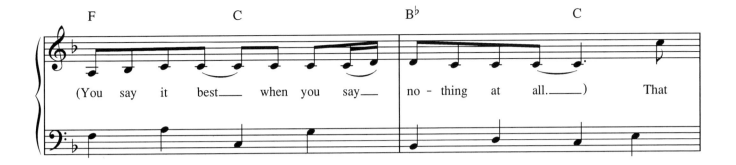

(You say it best___ when you say___ no - thing at all.___) That

smile on your face,___ there's truth in your eyes.___ The

touch of your hand___ lets me know___ that you need me.

Verse 2:

All day long I can hear people talking out loud
But when you hold me you drown out the crowd
Try as they may they can never defy
What's been said between your heart and mine.

The smile on your face *etc.*

You're My Number One

Words & Music by Mike Rose & Nick Foster

Moderately

Na na na na___ na na___ na na na___

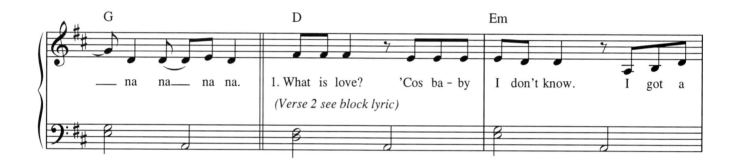

na na___ na na. 1. What is love? 'Cos ba - by I don't know. I got a

(Verse 2 see block lyric)

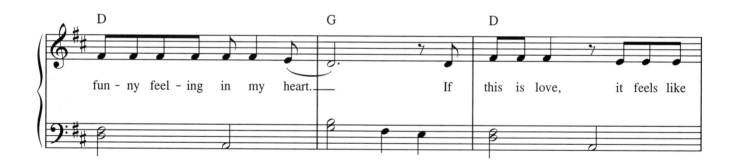

fun - ny feel - ing in my heart.___ If this is love, it feels like

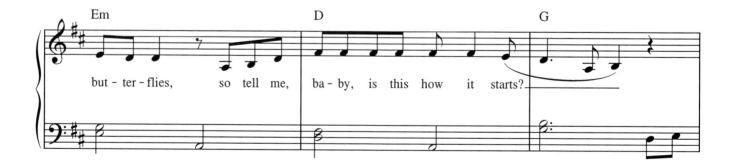

but - ter - flies, so tell me, ba - by, is this how it starts?___

I know I've nev - er felt like this be - fore,_____

you're like a drug, you got me want - ing more, I've got to__ let you know,____

I've got to let_____ you know.____

You're you're my num - ber one.___ I'd

do an - y - thing__ for you,___ catch the rain__ from the sky,__ ev - en hold__

back the tide for you baby, baby. You're

you're my number one. With you I know I belong.

I put the radio on and it's al-

- ways playing our song.

There ain't no - thing— I— won't— do,—

(Ooh_____) I'd walk on wa - ter just to be with you.—

D.S. Repeat Chorus to fade

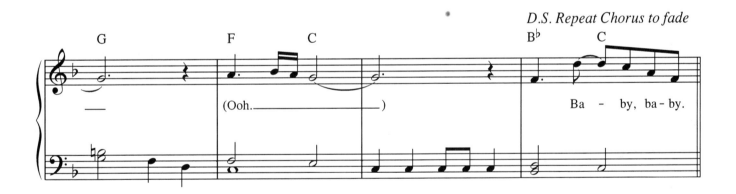

— (Ooh._____) Ba - by, ba - by.

Verse 2:

Tell me what, what have I gotta do?
'Cos I wanna lay a claim on you
To make you mine for now and for all time
So tell me, baby, what I gotta do
I know I've never felt like this before
You're like a drug, you got me wanting more
I've got to let you know
I've got to let you know.

You're, you're my number one *etc.*

Why Does It Always Rain On Me?

Words & Music by Fran Healy

Moderately

mf 1.3. I can't sleep to - night, ev - 'ry - bo - dy's say - ing

(Verse 2 see block lyric)

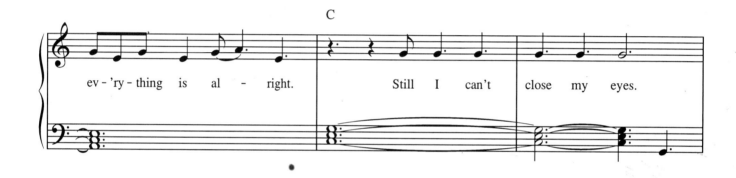

ev - 'ry - thing is al - right. Still I can't close my eyes.

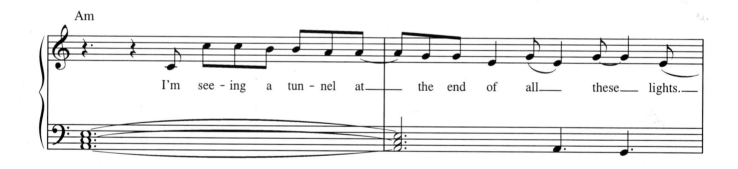

I'm see - ing a tun - nel at___ the end of all___ these___ lights.___

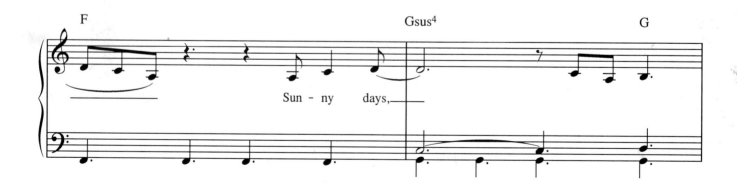

Sun - ny days,___

where have you gone?___ I___ get the stran - gest___ feel -

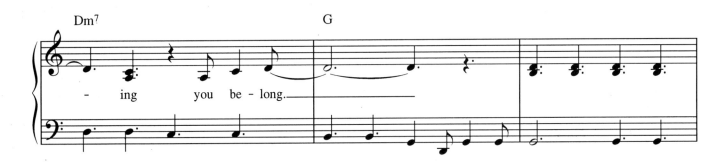

- ing you be - long.___

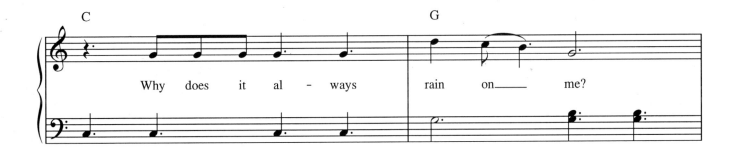

Why does it al - ways rain on___ me?

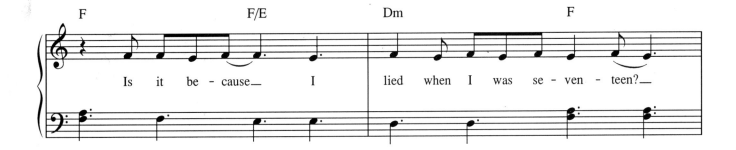

Is it be - cause___ I lied when I was se - ven - teen?___

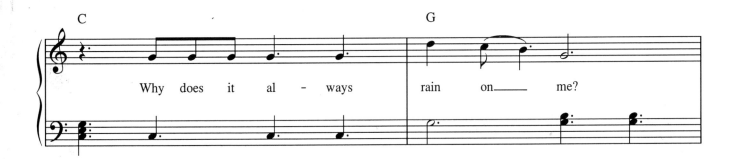

Why does it al - ways rain on___ me?

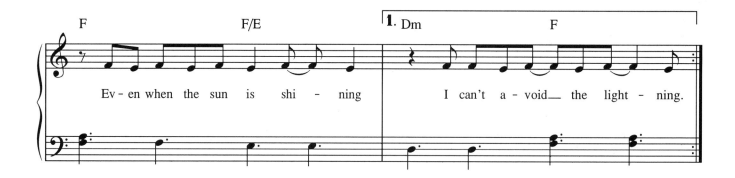

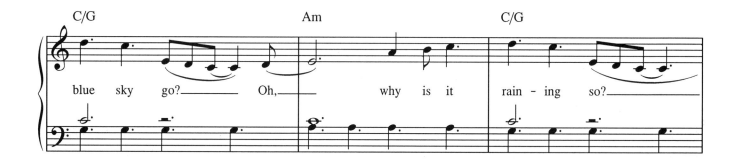

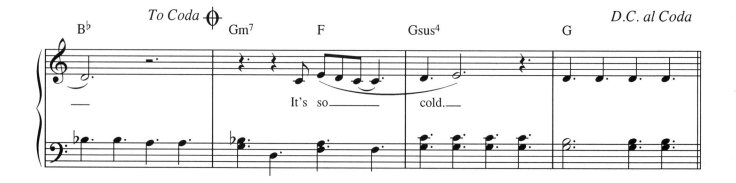

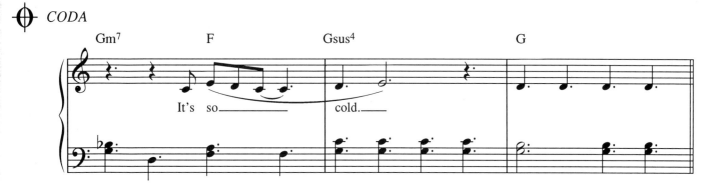

Gm⁷   F   Gsus⁴   G

It's so_____ cold.____

C   G   F

Why does it al - ways rain on___ me? Is it be - cause I

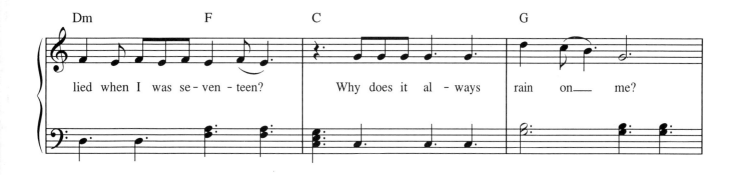

Dm   F   C   G

lied when I was se - ven - teen? Why does it al - ways rain on___ me?

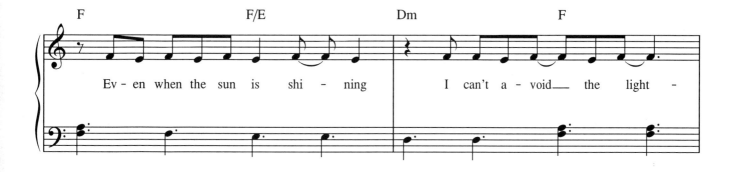

F   F/E   Dm   F

Ev - en when the sun is shi - ning I can't a - void___ the light -

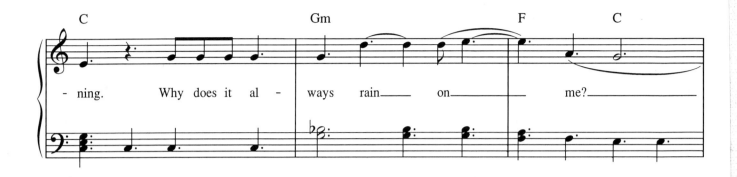

-ning. Why does it al - ways rain_____ on_____ me?_____

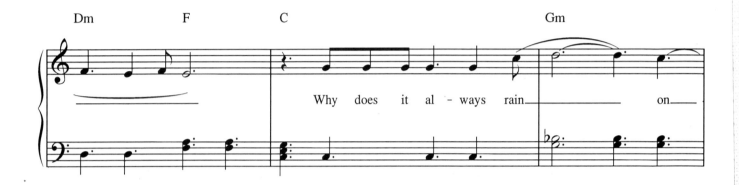

Why does it al - ways rain_____ on_____

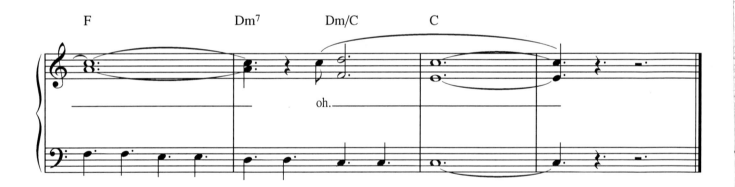

oh._____

Verse 2:

I can't stand myself
I'm being held up by invisible men
Still life on a shelf when
I got my mind on something else
Sunny days, where have you gone?
I get the strangest feeling you belong.

Why does it always rain on me *etc.*